The Directors of Forest of Dean Stone Firms Ltd. welcome you to this republished United Stone Firms prestigious book of 1912.

Founded in Bristol in 1910 United Stone Firms Ltd. set out to offer a wide range of UK and Irish stones under one banner. The new telegraph, telephone and delivery methods made them central in stone procurement. This exciting concept was launched just as Europe drifted into the ' War to end all Wars ', and hostilities saw the business fail in 1917. However, member companies traded on in administration and this led to The Forest of Dean Stone Firms Ltd. being re-registered at Companies House in 1922.

During 1926 United Stone Firms (1926) Ltd. was formed by a Walter Bryant. The business prospered, but the General Strike followed by the Wall Street Crash of 1929, and the 1930's Depression, saw the firm fold in 1932. Once again, member companies traded on whilst up for sale.

In February 1939 my grandfather Francis, and father Peter, were visiting South Wales looking for quarries to supply Silica. Their business was General Refractories Ltd. and with war looming, mineral bricks to line blast furnaces would be in huge demand. Snow was falling too thickly to get home to Cheltenham so they decided to stay at The Speech House Hotel in The Forest of Dean. The only other guest was the accountant acting for the Official Receiver, disposing of the assets of United Stone Firms.

By breakfast my family had bought the assets for £13,000. Within a week the scrap iron littering the various redundant premises had been sold and paid for the deal! Francis died in 1942, but under the stewardship of Elizabeth, his wife, and other family board members, The Forest of Dean Stone Firms Ltd. was the last company in family hands. In 2001, on the recommendation of Nicholas Horton, he and I purchased the company and set out to make it survive and prosper. In 2007 we were joined by Peter Hart and his family trust, and with investment in machinery, rebuilding, and marketing, the firm is looking forward to a rosy future.

Profitability and employment have grown many fold through enthusiasm and the high standards deserving of such an important mineral source.

Enjoy this book and try to picture the 'Golden Summer' of Edwardian England, bursting with hope and new technology, eclipsed by the most violent century in the history of the World. Today, we celebrate the endeavours of my forefathers in helping to shape the stone firm into the successful company that it is today.

M. Scott Russell

M. Scott Russell.
NOVEMBER 2012.

Forest of Dean Stone Firms Limited
Bixslade Stoneworks, Cannop Road, Parkend, Gloucestershire. GL15 4JS
Telephone: +44 (0)1594 562304 Facsimile: +44 (0)1594 564184
email: info@fodstone.co.uk Web site: www.fodstone.co.uk
The parent company of Forest Pennant

A UNIQUE SOURCE OF NATURAL PENNANT SANDSTONE

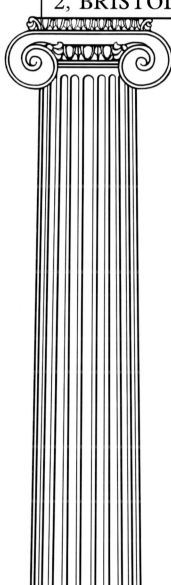

UNITED STONE FIRMS Ltd.

HEAD OFFICE,
2, BRISTOL CHAMBERS, NICHOLAS STREET, BRISTOL.

LONDON WORKS AND DEPOTS:

Addison Wharf, 191, Warwick Road, Kensington.
Imperial Wharf, 195, Warwick Road, Kensington.
Crown Wharf, 69, Lots Road, Chelsea.
Midland Railway Depot, Stewarts Road, Wandsworth.

LONDON OFFICE:

13, Buckingham Street, Strand, W.C.

PORTLAND OFFICE:

Park Road, Easton, Isle of Portland.

BELFAST OFFICE AND WORKS:

Harland Road, Musgrave Channel.

PLYMOUTH OFFICE:

Victoria Wharves, Sutton Road.

FOREST OF DEAN OFFICE:

Parkend, Near Lydney.

Telephone Numbers:		Telegraphic Addresses:	
Bristol	3910		Bristol
London Depots	1426 (Western)		London
London Office	1617 (Gerard)		
Portland ..	56	"MULTISTONE"	Portland
Belfast	3233		Belfast
Plymouth ..	1416		Plymouth
Parkend ..	4		

EDWARD EVERARD, PRINTER, BRISTOL.

UNITED STONE FIRMS, LTD.

Incorporates the following Firms:

FOREST OF DEAN STONE FIRMS, LTD.

Trotter Thomas & Co.   David & Sant, Ltd.

George Smith & Sons.   Porter Brothers.

Wilderness Brick & Stone Co., Ltd.

E. TURNER & SONS.

E. R. PAYNE & SONS, LTD.

PORTHGAIN QUARRIES, LTD.

Porthgain Harbour Ltd.

GEORGE A. WATSON & CO., LTD.

SOUTH LUOGH QUARRY CO., LTD.

ANDREWS & PROVIS.

HAM HILL QUARRIES.

HARD STONE FIRMS LTD.

The De Lank Granite Co.   The Bristol Pennant Stone Firms, Ltd.

Keinton Stone Co.   Joseph Seymour (Street).

GRICE & CO., LTD. (London).

DUKE & CO., LTD.

LISCANNOR QUARRY CO.

CHARLES ESSEX.

ALFRED FREE & SON.

NEW PORTLAND QUARRIES LTD.

Quarry Owners, producing the undermentioned materials:

PORTLAND STONE.

MOUNTCHARLES STONE.

GREY & BLUE FOREST OF DEAN STONE.

RED WILDERNESS STONE.

BATH STONE.

HAM HILL STONE.

NAILSWORTH STONE.

BLUE & RED BRISTOL PENNANT STONE.

KEINTON & STREET STONE.

SHAMROCK STONE.

DE LANK CORNISH GRANITE.

DARTMOOR GRANITE.

PORTHGAIN GRANITE (MACADAM & CHIPPINGS.)

INDEX.

GREY. FOREST OF DEAN STONE.

BLUE FOREST OF DEAN STONE.

Forest of Dean Stone.

The Quarries producing this well-known Sandstone are situated amidst magnificent woodland scenery in the Royal Forest of Dean, Gloucestershire, half-way between the Rivers Severn and Wye. They are connected with the Railway owned co-jointly by the Great Western and Midland Railway Companies. There are also excellent Docks at Lydney and Sharpness, where large quantities of stone are shipped.

There is little to record concerning the early history of the Forest of Dean Quarries, but appearances would lead to the belief that they are of great antiquity. There is evidence that some of the Quarries were worked by the Romans, and there are very old residences in the neighbourhood built with the stone, many of which are still in excellent preservation.

Although Forest of Dean Stone is known to have always commanded a ready sale as far back as is recorded, it is only during the last twenty years the Quarries have been extensively developed. During that period several large firms acquired Quarries and established Works in the district including the Forest of Dean Stone Firms, Ltd. (in which were incorporated David & Co., David & Sant, Ltd., Trotter, Thomas & Co., Porter Bros., and George Smith & Son); also Messrs. E. Turner & Sons, whose head offices were at Cardiff; and Messrs. E. R. Payne & Son, Ltd., whose head offices were at Newnham. The whole of these properties together with all the Plant, Machinery and Goodwill of the several businesses have now been acquired by the United Stone Firms, Ltd.

The Forest of Dean is owned by the Crown, from whom Quarries are leased at a fixed annual rental, which merges into a royalty. There is a very curious and ancient forest law in connection with the taking out of these leases, or gales, as they are locally termed. The Crown has only the power to grant these gales to bona fide freeminers, and a freeminer is one who was born in the Hundred of St. Briavels, and has worked a year and a day in either a quarry, coal mine, or iron mine. Upon attaining the age of twenty-one, he is duly registered as a freeminer by the Deputy Gaveller, at the Crown Offices, Coleford. He has then the right to apply for a tract of minerals, and if no one has previously applied for the same, he may work these minerals, for his own profit, subject to the payment of certain annual rents and royalties to the Crown, and subject to certain other conditions too lengthy to mention here. There is no certain record of the origin of these freeminers' rights, which are referred to in the oldest deeds as "privileges time out of mind". They are, however, generally supposed to have been granted in the early part of the fourteenth century, for services rendered to the King in his battles with the rebellious Scots—the Foresters at that period being skilful archers as well as miners.

Visitors to the Forest of Dean in the summer will, in addition to being welcomed by the Officials of the Company, and escorted around their Quarries and Works, find many other items of interest in the neighbourhood. In the centre of the Forest stands

POINT QUARRIES, FETTERHILL, FOREST OF DEAN

the celebrated Speche House, which formerly was the Royal Court of Justice, and it was here that the "Jovial Foresters" were tried and sentenced for poaching the deer and, some say, for shooting the keepers, in the good old days. There are still some very old customs kept up here, notably the "Court Leet," which is remarkable for the fact that it is the oldest court in England, having been instituted in the reign of King Canute. The principal business of this court, at the present time, is to settle questions of encroachment on the Crown Land; but it can be imagined that formerly the business transacted was not of so civil a nature. The Court Room is in a good state of preservation, and contains many relics of bygone days. The Speche House is now an hotel and has the further distinction, so it is said, of being one out of the only two licensed houses in the country belonging to the Crown, the other being situate at Symonds Yat, also near the Forest of Dean. The scenery in this vicinity is some of the finest in the country. Close by is the magnificent valley of the Wye, justly termed the Switzerland of England, with its noted views at Symonds Yat, the Buckstone, and Double View, all of which are visited annually by thousands of tourists and pleasure seekers. The Forest trees are second to none in Britain, in size and beauty, and point the truth of the old saying, "Blessed is the eye, twixt the Severn and the Wye."

The principal stone producing districts are the Bixhead, Fetterhill, Cannop, Knockley and Wimberry Valleys. The stone is obtained in two distinct colours, Grey and Blue. The beds of stone in the Quarries vary considerably in thickness, frequently jumping and losing themselves in a most remarkable manner, and it is impossible to determine with certainty how any particular lift will turn out. Generally speaking six feet may be taken as a fair average of the beds found, but they are often ten feet thick, and sometimes as much as fifteen feet thick. There is little or no inclination or pitch in the beds, and the Quarries are much divided by vertical and parallel joints, which greatly facilitate quarrying operations. The stone is conveyed from the Quarries to the different loading sidings by means of trams drawn by horses. The tramways are from half a mile to one and a half miles in length and are constructed with the old-fashioned angle-plate rails. Horse traction is essential owing to the very steep gradient and sharp curves down the valleys, but a team of horses will take from twenty-five to thirty tons on a single journey. Shoes and sprags are used on the trams, and great care and experience are necessary adjuncts to the qualifications of the spraggers in charge.

The Works for sawing and dressing the stone, are established alongside the Railways in the different Valleys. There are large works at Parkend, Cannop (Speech House Road), Bixslade, Fetterhill, Point and Knockley. All these Works are splendidly equipped with Modern Machinery of every description, comprising Sand and Water Saw Frames, Circular Saws, Planing and Moulding Machines, Rubbing Tables, Lathes, and every other requisite necessary for cutting and finishing every description of stonework. These Works are directly connected with the Railways by Sidings, and each Works have accommodation

BIXHEAD No. 3 QUARRY, FOREST OF DEAN

FOREST OF DEAN STONE—Continued.

for a large number of Banker Masons. The quantity of Machinery at the several Mills is enormous, so much so, that the Company is able to undertake building or engineering orders of any magnitude, and to guarantee the prompt and satisfactory execution of any quantity of stonework in any sizes.

Forest of Dean Stone is extensively used in all parts of the country for all kinds of work, being renowned for exceptional strength and durability, also uniformity of colour and texture, which it always retains.

For Building purposes it cannot be surpassed, and excellent examples are found in many of the most important Public Buildings, Churches, Post Offices, County Courts, Libraries, Asylums, Markets, Workhouses, Gaols, as well as large Residences in all parts of the United Kingdom. In South Wales it is recognised as the only economical material which will weather satisfactorily and retain its natural colour in the trying smoky and chemical atmosphere of the Welsh Valleys.

For the general Building trade, there is an enormous daily call for Steps, and Landings, Window Sills, Copings, Templates, Bases and all general work.

As an Engineering Stone it is in great demand, and it has been used in nearly all the important Engineering Works in the West of England and South Wales. The piers and abutments of the Severn Bridge are of Forest of Dean Stone, and here the Stone has to stand a very severe and unique test, inasmuch as it is exposed every twelve hours to salt and fresh water, and the atmosphere alternately, but the piers are still in a perfect state of preservation. Large quantities of the Stone were used in the construction of the Severn Tunnel for the Great Western Railway. Amongst other important works are the Docks at Cardiff, Swansea, Bristol, Newport, Sharpness, Gloucester, Barry, Port Talbot, Watchet Harbour and other places; Waterworks at Blagdon (Somerset), Cardiff, Malvern, Neath, Briton Ferry, Mountain Ash, Aberdare, etc.; Gas Tank at St. Philip's, Bristol, erected in 1892 (which when completed was the largest outside London), also Gasworks at Cardiff, Gloucester, Cheltenham, Cirencester, Swansea, etc. All the principal Railway Companies have used the stone extensively for Bridges, Viaducts, Tunnels and Station Buildings. Engine Bed Blocks and Foundation Stones are a speciality, and are extensively supplied to Collieries, Iron and Steel Works, and other large industries throughout the country.

The Blue Forest of Dean Stone is famed for Monumental, Architectural and Carving purposes, and it is economical to work, weathers clean, and keeps its natural colour. Thousands of Headstones are despatched annually to all parts, and it is purchased by Sculptors in preference to any other stone.

Staircases are being constantly prepared out of the hard Blue Beds, for which it is one of the finest materials obtainable. It is largely supplied to the Office of Works, for Staircases; also to the Government Departments, and to many of the leading Architects

OAK QUARRY, No. 1, FOREST OF DEAN

FOREST OF DEAN STONE—Continued.

for Steps and Landings of Public Buildings.   For these purposes, it wears exceptionally well. and does not get slippery, besides which the stone is inexpensive.

ANALYSIS.

Silica (partly free and partly combined)	80.16
Alumina (combined with Silica)	14.40
Oxide of Iron	1.65
Carbonate of Lime	2.55
Magnesia	.24
Sulphate of Lime...	1.00
	——————
	100.00
	——————

Crushing Strain (Kirkaldy) 631 tons to the square foot.

COFFEE PIT QUARRIES, FOREST OF DEAN.

OAK QUARRIES, FOREST OF DEAN.

CUTTING

BLOCK

STONE

AT

SPION

KOP

QUARRY,

FOREST

OF

DEAN

BIXHEAD NO. 1 QUARRY, FOREST OF DEAN

CANNOP WORKS, SPEECH HOUSE ROAD, FOREST OF DEAN.

BIRCH HILL QUARRY, FOREST OF DEAN.

10

PARKEND WORKS, FOREST OF DEAN.

SPION KOP QUARRIES, FOREST OF DEAN

HOWLERS HILL QUARRY, FOREST OF DEAN

PARKEND WORKS, FOREST OF DEAN.

KNOCKLEY QUARRIES, Nos. 2 and 3, FOREST OF DEAN

FETTERHILL WORKS, FOREST OF DEAN.

MACHINERY AT FETTERHILL WORKS, FOREST OF DEAN.

POINT WORKS, FOREST OF DEAN.

BIXSLADE WORKS, FOREST OF DEAN.

STANHOPE HOUSE, PARK LANE, W.
Built Wholly of Grey Forest of Dean Stone
Architects: Messrs. Romaine, Walker & Besant.

HARBORNE POLICE AND FIRE STATION, BIRMINGHAM.
GREY FOREST OF DEAN STONE.

Architect: City Surveyor of Birmingham

CONSERVATIVE CLUB, TREHERBERT.
BLUE FOREST OF DEAN STONE.

Architect: Jacob Rees, Esq.

BARRACKS FOR EIGHT BATTALIONS C

RED WILDERNESS STONE FOR DRESSINGS TO OFFICERS' QUARTERS AND INTERNAL STAIRCASES   BLUE

The whole of the Stonework for this huge contract

ANTRY, TIDWORTH, SALISBURY PLAIN
OF DEAN STONE THROUGHOUT ALL OTHER BUILDINGS FOR DRESSINGS, ALSO FOR STEPS AND LANDINGS.
pplied from our Quarries and Dressed at our Works

NEW SESSIONS HOUSE, NEWGATE STREET, E.C.
BLUE FOREST OF DEAN STONE FOR INTERNAL STAIRCASES.

BRIDGE OVER CANAL AT SPARKBROOK, BIRMINGHAM
MAIN ARCH IN COURSE OF ERECTION
Blue Forest of Dean Stone.

THE CELEBRATED SEVERN BRIDGE.
FOREST OF DEAN STONE.

LITTLETON BRIDGE, NEAR SHEPPERTON.
GREY FOREST OF DEAN STONE DRESSINGS AND RED WILDERNESS STONE FACINGS
Engineer: H. T. Wakelam, County Surveyor of Middlesex.

CARNEGIE LIBRARY BRIDGEND.
BLUE FOREST OF DEAN STONE.

20, OLD CAVENDISH STREET, W.,
FOR J. R. W. SOPER, ESQ.
BLUE FOREST OF DEAN STONE.
Architects: Messrs. Bulman & Dear

SUBWAYS, NEW G.W.R. STATION, SNOW HILL, BIRMINGHAM,
IN COURSE OF ERECTION.
BLUE FOREST OF DEAN GIRDER BED STONES.

BLOCK
OF
PREMISES,
BELFAST.

GREY
FOREST
OF
DEAN
STONE.

Architect:
W. J. Gilliland, Esq.

SNOW HILL
G.W.R. STATION,
BIRMINGHAM,

COMPLETED
SUBWAY.

BLUE
FOREST
OF
DEAN
STONE
FOR
BEDSTONES,
BASES,
PADSTONES, Etc.

POLICE AND FIRE STATION, BORDESLEY GREEN, BIRMINGHAM.
GREY FOREST OF DEAN STONE

COUNCIL OFFICES, PONTYPRIDD, GLAM.
GREY FOREST OF DEAN STONE.
Architect: Henry T. Hare, Esq., Bloomsbury, W.C.

BRIDGE OVER CANAL, SPARKBROOK, BIRMINGHAM.
Blue Forest of Dean Stone Arch and Dressings

BLUE FOREST OF DEAN COPING,
NEW G.W.R. STATION, SNOW HILL, BIRMINGHAM.

ENTRANCE TO PUBLIC PARK, STAPLE HILL, BRISTOL.

BOUNDARY WALLS, RED PENNANT SHODDIES WITH BLUE PENNANT COPING THE PILLARS AND CAPS ARE OF
BLUE FOREST OF DEAN STONE

Architect: J. A. Wright, Esq

APPROACH TO SMALL HEATH BRIDGE, BIRMINGHAM

BLUE FOREST OF DEAN CAPS AND COPINGS.

NEW GRAVING DOCK, AVONMOUTH, BRISTOL.
FOREST OF DEAN STONE ASHLAR.

Docks Engineer: W. W. Squire, Esq.

ROYAL EDWARD DOCK, AVONMOUTH, BRISTOL
FOREST OF DEAN STONE STEPS AND ASHLAR COPINGS

ALTAR, ST. GREGORY'S R.C. CHURCH, EARLSFIELD, S.W.
NAILSWORTH AND BLUE FOREST OF DEAN STONE ALTERNATELY.

BLAGDON WATER-WORKS: VIEW OF TUNNEL OUTLET FACE
Grey Forest of Dean Stone.

BLAGDON RESERVOIR, SOMERSETSHIRE: THE BYEWASH.
All the Ashlar for this Work, and also the Pitching, Cillstones and Steps are of Forest of Dean Stone

BRISTOL WATERWORKS AT BLAGDON, SOMERSETSHIRE: THE BRIDGE OVER THE BYEWASH.
Forest of Dean Stone.
Engineers: Messrs. T. & C. Hawksley

RED WILDERNESS STONE.

Red Wilderness Stone.

The Quarries producing this celebrated Stone were previously the property of the Forest of Dean Stone Firms, Ltd., who acquired them from the Wilderness Brick & Stone Co,. Ltd.

It is quarried exclusively at Mitcheldean, GIoucestershire, where the Works are also situated, and is unquestionably the finest Red Stone in the Country.

This rock belongs to the old Red Sandstone formation, but is more compact than the generality of this stone, and is of good colour, which it always retains.   It is of very fine texture, and great hardness.

For all classes of Building, Engineering and Monumental purposes, it is extensively used, and is most beautiful and attractive for all external work.   It weathers well in any atmosphere and its durability is beyond question or doubt. This stone is also specially adapted for internal work, for which it is in great demand, on account of its warm colour and its superior finish and appearance.   For paving work, it is very attractive, especially when intermixed with other colour stones.   It makes excellent Piers, Bases, Caps, Columns and internal dressings of all kinds.

The thin beds of the Quarries can be worked into Shoddies at a very low cost, and it is a colour which blends with other materials, or in fact can be used to advantage and satisfaction for any purpose.

The blocks can be readily obtained in any sizes and quantities, and large stocks of stone are always on hand ready for despatch, or to be sawn or worked up to any dimensions or design.

A list of numerous important Buildings in which the stone has been used in all parts of the country can be obtained on application.

ANALYSIS.

Silica (Quartz)	... ...	88.70
Alumina	... ...	3.25
Ferric Oxide	... ...	1.80
Ferrous Oxide	... ...	.30
Manganese	... ...	.10
Lime ...	... ...	2.90
Magnesia ...	... ...	.11
Carbonic Acid	... ...	1.94
Alkalies ...	... ...	.31
Loss ...	... ...	.59
		100.00

Crushing Strain (Kirkaldy) 695 tons to the square foot.

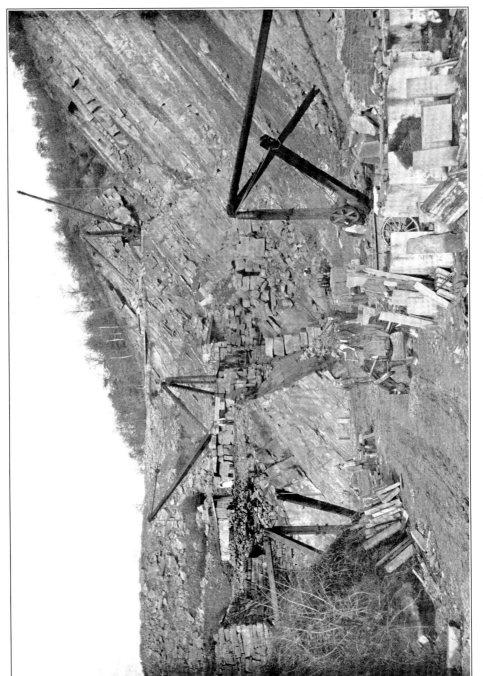

A GENERAL VIEW OF THE WILDERNESS QUARRIES

ABBENHALL LODGE, MITCHELDEAN, THE RESIDENCE
OF J. W. PROBYN, ESQ., J.P.
RED WILDERNESS STONE.

RESIDENCE OF FRANCIS WINTLE, ESQ., MITCHELDEAN.
RED WILDERNESS STONE.

BLOCK OF PREMISES, HANS CRESCENT,
BROMPTON ROAD, S.W.

RED WILDERNESS STONE.

CAMERON HOTEL, SWANSEA.
GROUND FLOOR, RED WILDERNESS STONE.
Architect: Charles T. Ruthen, Esq.

HIGHER GRADE SCHOOLS AT ABERDARE, GLAMORGANSHIRE.
RED WILDERNESS STONE DRESSINGS THROUGHOUT.
Architect: T. Roderick, Esq.

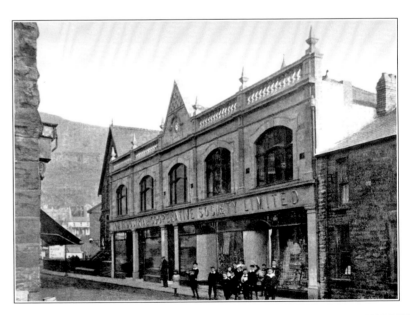

CO-OPERATIVE SOCIETY'S BUILDINGS, TON PENTRE, RHONDDA VALLEY
RED WILDERNESS PILESTONES, GREY FOREST OF DEAN DRESSINGS.
Architect: W. D. Morgan, Esq. M. S. A.

PREMISES, QUEEN STREET, CARDIFF, FOR
MESSRS. JOHN WILLIAMS & SONS.
RED WILDERNESS STONE.
Architect: Edwin Seward, Esq.

HAM HILL STONE.

Ham Hill Stone.

It is considered by many people that Ham Hill is the prettiest Building Stone obtainable in this country.

These extensive Quarries were until recently worked by the Ham Hill and Doulting Stone Co., but upon the expiry of the leases they were taken over by us and have since been very considerably developed. They are situate on the summit of Ham Hill, near Montacute Station, G.W.R., in the County of Somerset, and at this station the Stone is put on rail.

It is a Stone of mottled appearance and yellow tint which is considered a warm rich colour and harmonises readily in any surroundings. The Quarries are very old and have furnished the Stonework for most of the renowned Towers and Churches in the West Country, and also many of the Mansions and important Buildings in the South and West of England. The present condition of these Buildings affords the best proof of the enduring qualities of the Stone.

To Architects requiring a reliable Stone (superior to Bath Stone in weathering qualities, and of equal cost and durability to Doulting and less costly than Portland), then Ham Hill Stone supplies this want. The crushing strain of Ham Hill Stone is 207 tons to the square foot, which is considerably more than Ancaster, and other softer stones, yet it compares favourably in cost. It is impervious to atmospheric influences.

Adjoining the Quarries are large Works fitted with Saws, Planing and Moulding Machines for sawing and working the Stone, with extensive Masonry Shops all under cover where work can be carried on continuously in any weather, thereby reducing our prices for Dressed Stone to a minimum and enabling us to guarantee prompt delivery of any sizes and quantities.

The Stone is a pleasing colour and quality for internal work and is still in great demand for interiors as well as external elevations and dressings of all kinds.

Sawn or Dressed Stone is recommended in preference to Random Block out of this material, as owing to its nature the waste in the conversion of Block is rather more than with our other Building Stones.

No 1 QUARRY, HAM HILL.

No. 2 QUARRY, HAM HILL, WITH GENERAL VIEW OF WORKS.

No. 3 QUARRY, HAM HILL.

QUARRYING STONE AT HAM HILL.

A MASONRY SHOP AT HAM HILL QUARRIES.

PLANING AND MOULDING MACHINES, HAM HILL.

SAWING MACHINERY AT HAM HILL.

TRAVELLERS'
CLUB,
PICCADILLY, W.

HAM
HILL
STONE
THROUGHOUT

RESIDENCE AT HARROW.

HAM HILL STONE.

Architect: Arnold Mitchell, Esq., Hanover Square, W.

RESIDENCE AT HARROW.
HAM HILL STONE.

Architect: Arnold Mitchell, Esq.

40

GARDENS AT EASTON LODGE, DUNMOW, ESSEX, THE SEAT OF THE COUNTESS OF WARWICK.
Ham Hill Stone Throughout.

Architect: H. A. Peto, Esq., Bradford-on-Avon

41

BRYMPTON HOUSE, THE SEAT OF THE HON. SIR SPENCER C. B. PONSONBY FANE, K.C.B.
The exact day of erection is not known, but it was built in the time of John Sydenham II, about 1470—1543
Various additions have been made since, notably the Garden Front from designs by
the celebrated Architect: Inigo Jones.
HAM HILL STONE

MONTACUTE HOUSE, SEAT OF W. R. PHILIPS ESQ., J.P., D.L.
ENTIRELY OF HAM HILL STONE.
Built between the years 1580—1601 by Sir Edward Philips, Master of the Rolls and Speaker in the House of Commons,
and has continuously been in the hands of the same family. The long Gallery is 189 feet long and 21 feet wide.
The house is built in the form of letter E both East and West sides. In the Second Storey, in the spaces between
the windows are eight beautifully carved statues in Ham Hill Stone and said to represent the nine worthies.

UNIVERSITY COLLEGE SCHOOLS, HAMPSTEAD.
DRESSINGS THROUGHOUT AND BOUNDARY WALLS OF HAM HILL STONE.

UNIVERSITY COLLEGE SCHOOLS, HAMPSTEAD.
HAM HILL STONE.

HAM HILL STONE SUN-DIAL

EAST STOKE CHURCH, SOMERSET.
NORMAN DESIGN.

Said to be one of the oldest Churches in England.

ENTIRELY BUILT OF HAM HILL STONE AND IN EXCELLENT
PRESERVATION.

HAM HILL STONE FIREPLACE, NORTH PERROTT
MANOR HOUSE

NAILSWORTH STONE.

Nailsworth Stone.

Until acquired by this company these Quarries were held by Messrs. Andrews & Provis, of Coleford, and Mr. C. Essex, of Avening, near Stroud.

The Stone is very little known to Architects and Surveyors owing to the Quarries having been worked almost entirely for local purposes during the past few years, but the enormous underground headings prove that at some time most extensive quarrying operations must have been carried on by our forebears.

The Quarries are situated at Balls Green, near Nailsworth, in Gloucestershire. They have always been worked underground, but upon an antiquated system. We have recently introduced the modern methods of quarrying which are in vogue at the Bath Stone Quarries, which besides cheapening the cost of production yields a larger average size, greatly increases the output and gives excellent results in every way. The Stone is of oolite formation, and resembles Portland in quality and appearance so much so that the difference is hardly discernable. It is very considerably cheaper, and great hopes are entertained that when it is well known it will be extensively used in London and the Provinces.

The possibilities of these Quarries are enormous. The beds of rock are entirely free from defects, and can be obtained in hugh sizes, thus giving a splendid average cubical measurement for Random Block. It is very mild working when freshly quarried, but hardens very considerably and quickly, when brought to the surface, and is very hard after a few week's exposure, when the moisture has evaporated.

It is an excellent durable Stone for external and internal purposes, and weathers well. It is a particularly desirable Stone where cost is a consideration, as it can be supplied at a very low finished cost without any risk as to strength, quality and durability.

We desire to call the attention of all Architects to this material and solicit a trial. For external elevations, also internal work, and for residential staircases it will be found to give great satisfaction.

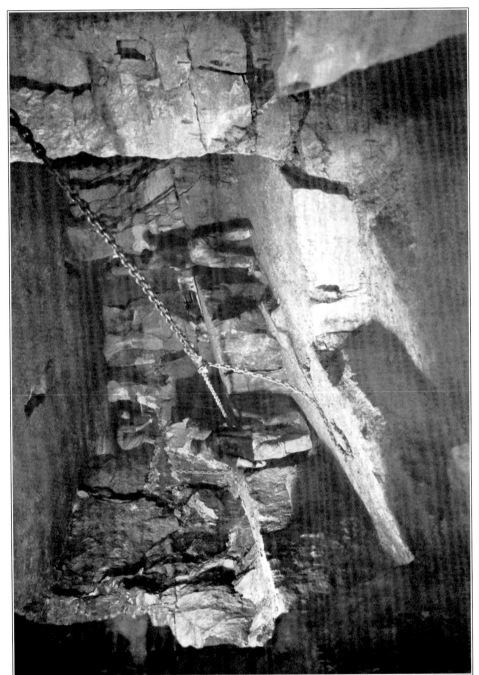

VIEW OF QUARRYING OPERATIONS UNDERGROUND AT NAILSWORTH.

UNDERGROUND QUARRYING AT NAILSWORTH.

MASONIC TEMPLE, ABERAVON, GLAM.
NAILSWORTH STONE.
Joint Architects: Messrs. J. A. James & Thomas Gibb.

ST. MICHAEL'S CHURCH, YEOVIL
HAM HILL STONE.
Architect: J. Nicholson Johnson, Esq., Yeovil.

STACKING GROUND, OFFICES, AND ENTRANCE TO UNDERGROUND WORKINGS
BALLS GREEN QUARRIES, NAILSWORTH.

Portland Stone.

A writer in 1732, of a work entitled " A Particular Survey of the Countie of Dorset," speaks of the discovery of Portland Stone as being about the year 1600.

There is, however, evidence to show that Portland Stone was in use many years before this. It would be more correct to say that it came into repute about this time. We know that, by the advice of his Architect, King James made choice of Portland Stone for building his Banqueting House at Whitehall about the year 1610.

From this time it has been in continuous and increasing demand.

It is certain that it has proved itself to be one of the best weather resisting stones known. In all positions it has satisfactorily stood all kinds of atmospheric influence, and to-day stands approved as a safe and excellent quality Building Stone.

This is endorsed by most of the leading Architects and Stone Experts of to-day, and in support of this, the following extracts from " The Builder " and " The Building News " may be given.

" It is well known that the beauties of many stone buildings (in London and other smoke laden atmospheres) are absolutely effaced by dirt in a very short time, but if constructed with Portland Stone they improve with age and dirt in London."

" The only material which is absolutely improved by smoke, especially if the style employed is columnar, is Portland STONE."

" The river front of Somerset House, in its beautiful stone and stately style, presents one of the most dignified aspects in the City of London,"

The best testimonial, however, is found in the buildings which have stood the test of time, of which St. Paul's Cathedral stands a notable example.

Besides these public and national buildings, the two Castles in the Island of Portland may be instanced in proof of its perfect weathering qualities. One called " Rufus Castle," built about the end of the Eleventh Century, and the other called " The Portland Castle " built by Henry VIII about the year 1520. Both these stand close to the sea, and exposed to the severest weather, yet the stone to-day is in perfect preservation, even showing the marks of the workmen's tools. Ancient records of the Island refer to supplies of stone to Mr. Christopher Wren for St. Paul's Cathedral and his fifty churches. The geology of the Portland Stone beds was very little understood at that time, and a fear was expressed that, the stone would be exhausted before the buildings would be completed. So strong was this conviction that a proclamation was made by the King's authority,

SILKLAKE QUARRIES, WAKEHAM, ISLE OF PORTLAND

PORTLAND STONE—Continued.

forbidding any person to transport stone from the Island of Portland without the permission of Mr. Christopher Wren, the Surveyor General.   Date : May 4th, 1669.   Although the stone could be seen in the cliffs, it was not known that, the whole of this higher part of the Island was one solid bed of stone.   This stone area consists of about 2,500 acres, with beds from twelve to twenty feet deep.   Although since that time, many hundreds of thousands of tons have been exported, there still remains sufficient at the present rate of export, for from 500 to a 1,000 years' supply.

A business like the United Stone Firms, Ltd., would not be complete without a Portland Stone Section.   Appreciating this, the firm has acquired the Business and Quarries of the New Portland Quarries, Limited.   In addition they have also secured further large areas of land from various owners for the opening of new Quarries, which are now being very rapidly and extensively developed and equipped with powerful steam cranes and all the latest quarrying devices.   The districts chosen contain the very best stone in the Island.   Provision is being made for a very large increase in the production of stone from these Quarries, and as the quality of the stone is very superior, it is certain that a large share of the future trade of the Island will be secured.

Stone from these particular Quarries has been used in many first-class buildings, amongst which may be mentioned the following :—

> The Naval Barracks at Chatham.
> The Victoria Barracks at Portsmouth.
> Charing Cross Hospital, London.
> Messrs. Wilkinsons Sword Co's. Buildings, 25, Pall Mall.
> The Fine Premises at 9 and 10, Pall Mall.
> Public Library at Bow E.
> St. Jude's Church at Hampstead.
> Wellington Hotel, Strand
> Public Schools (L.C.C.) Rotherhithe and Cow Lane.
> Lloyd's Bank at Dover.
> Tram Sheds at Birmingham.

In the Island of Portland where Stone for Public Buildings has to meet the approval of special local experts, Stone from these Quarries has been chosen and used in the following Buildings :—

> New Naval Hospital.
> New Wesleyan Church at Easton.
> The Clock Tower in Easton Square Gardens.
> A handsome Elizabethan Dwelling House in Easton Square.
The Local Offices in the Island of Portland are situate at Park Road, Easton.

Nos. 1 and 2 QUARRIES, ABOVE COOMBE, ISLE OF PORTLAND.

PARK QUARRIES, NEAR EASTON STATION, ISLE OF PORTLAND

Nos. 1 and 2 QUARRIES, WAKEHAM, ISLE OF PORTLAND.

QUARRIES AT EASTON, ISLE OF PORTLAND.

GRAMMARS LANDS, ISLE OF PORTLAND, IN THE COOBMEFIELD DISTRICT
RECENTLY ACQUIRED FOR QUARRYING OPERATIONS.

OPENING A NEW QUARRY AT GRAMMARS LAWNS, WESTON ISLE OF PORTLAND

NAVAL BARRACKS, CHATHAM.
Portland Stone Dressings From Coombe Quarries.

NAVAL HOSPITAL, ISLE OF PORTLAND.
Portland Stone Dressings From Our Quarries.

CLOCK TOWER AND WESLEYAN CHURCH, THE SQUARE,
EASTON, ISLE OF PORTLAND.

THE WHOLE OF THE PORTLAND STONE IN BOTH STRUCTURES WAS
OBTAINED FROM OUR QUARRIES.

NEW EXTENSIONS, CHARING CROSS HOSPITAL, W.C.
PORTLAND STONE FROM OUR QUARRIES

PUBLIC
LIBRARY,
BOW, E.

PORTLAND
STONE.

ENTRANCE TO ROMANO'S RESTAURANT,
PORTLAND STONE WORK EXECUTED BY US.

LLOYDS BANK, DOVER.
BUILT ENTIRELY OF OUR PORTLAND STONE.

CHAPEL AT NEW TREDEGAR, IN COURSE OF ERECTION.
Dressed Portland Stone from our Quarries and Works.

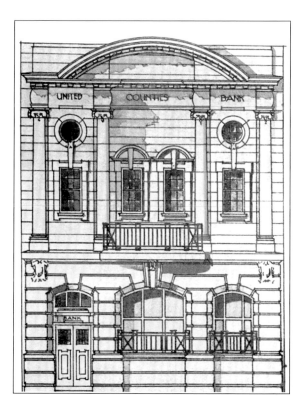

UNITED COUNTIES BANK, LEICESTER.
De Lank Granite Basement,
Bath Stone Superstructure.
Architects: Messrs. A. E. & T. Sawday

9 AND 10, PALL MALL, W.
Built of Our Portland Stone.

Bath Stone.

This material is so well known throughout the building trade that no introduction is considered necessary.

The mineral won is from the estate of Colonel Northey. The Quarries are all underground and the shaft up which it is brought to the surface is situate at Longsplatt on Box Hill, a short distance from Box Great Western Railway Station. The Block Stone is conveyed from the workings upon trams, and hauled up the shaft with winding gear. A depot has been established on the surface where large quantities of seasoned Block Stone are always kept in stock. Masonry Shops have been erected at this depot, and every description of worked Bath Stone is prepared ready for fixing, which is loaded into railway trucks at Box Station and distributed to all parts of the country.

The quality of the Bath Stone obtained from these Quarries is exceptionally good and quite equal in durability and strength to other " brands " on the market, either for external or internal purposes.

QUARRYING BATH STONE (UNDERGROUND OPERATIONS) AT LONGSPLATT QUARRIES.

ANOTHER UNDERGROUND WORKING FACE AT LONGSPLATT QUARRIES

STACKING GROUND FOR BATH STONE, LONGSPLATT QUARRIES, BOX.

ALBANY ROAD WESLEYAN CHURCH CARDIFF.
Bath Stone Dressings from Our Longsplatt Quaries.

BISHOP'S PALACE, ABERGWLI, NORTH WALES.
BATH STONE FROM LONGSPLATT QUARRIES.

OFFICES FOR MESSRS. JOHN CORY & SONS, LTD., DOCKS, CARDIFF
LONGSPLATT BATH STONE DRESSINGS.

MOUNTCHARLES STONE.

Mountcharles Stone.

These Quarries and Works have been acquired from G. A. Watson & Co., Ltd., together with the goodwill and all effects.

The Stone is quarried at Mountcharles, County Donegal, in the North of Ireland.

It is of a warm cream colour, and bleaches white after a few years' exposure. It is one of the finest sandstones obtainable, and in appearance, as well as in weathering qualities, cannot be surpassed. This is well known and appreciated in Ireland, where there are many excellent examples, several of the largest and finest buildings having been constructed with this stone, including Letterkenny Cathedral, Dublin Museum, and innumerable Churches, Banks, and Public Buildings.

Hitherto the difficulty has been to obtain sufficient supplies, but we have taken steps to remedy this, and are now working and developing the Quarries with the most modern lifting and stoneworking machinery and appliances, in such a way as to ensure prompt delivery of any demands. This will also considerably reduce the cost. We are assured this will command practically the whole of the Irish Building trade, as in that country the Stone is held in such high esteem that it is preferred to any other material.

This stone is practically unknown in England, and we are anxious to introduce it into the British markets. We have confidence that when it has been used in a few buildings in London and the Provinces it will become as popular in this country as it is in Ireland, for in appearance and in every other way it is the most beautiful Building Stone obtainable in the United Kingdom. The facility for delivery is all that can be desired, as a pier adjoins the Quarries, where the stone can be loaded direct into our own steamers, and conveyed to England at the bare cost of water transit.

Its superiority over ordinary sandstones is explained by the fact that it is a felspathic grit rather than a normal sandstone, and was evidently derived from a granite rock of a good weathering character, and thus possessing points which are exceptionally favourable to its durability as a building stone, such as the remarkable freshness of the accessory minerals, viz. : Felspar ; the evidence of Silification as shown in the Secondary Silica ; the deposition of Secondary Calcite as isolated crystals, and not as cementing materials ; and absence of lamination. Moreover, it can be worked to any desired finish.

We especially recommend this exceptional quality stone to Architects and Engineers for consideration.

ANALYSIS.

Silica	76.76
Alumina	11.13
Ferrous Oxide	.15
Ferric Oxide	.50
Lime	1.25
Magnesia	.59
Potassium Oxide	3.72
Sodium Oxide	2.47
Loss on Ignition	2.95
	———
	99.52

Crushing Strain (Kirkaldy) 772 tons to the square foot.

MOUNTCHARLES QUARRIES, CO. DONEGAL.

CRANE-ROAD TO QUARRY FACE AT MOUNTCHARLES.

MASONS' SHEDS, MOUNTCHARLES WORKS, CO. DONEGAL

MOUNTCHARLES PIER, CO. DONEGAL.

NEW CHURCH, CLONARD MONASTERY, BELFAST.
Mountcharles Cut Stone and Shamrock Stone Shoddies Throughout.
Architect: J. J. McDonnell Esq.

LETTERKENNY CATHEDRAL, CO. DONEGAL.
BUILT ENTIRELY OF MOUNTCHARLES STONE EXTERNALLY AND INTERNALLY

R.C. CHURCH, ARDARA, CO. DONEGAL.
MOUNTCHARLES STONE.

ULSTER BANK, LURGAN, CO. ARMAGH.
MOUNTCHARLES STONE.

Architect: Vincent Craig, Esq.

CORK CITY RAILWAYS AND BRIDGES
ABUTMENT IN COURSE OF ERECTION   MOUNTCHARLES STONE.

ULSTER BANK, MOUNT POLLINGER, BELFAST
MOUNTCHARLES STONE.
Architects : Messrs. Blackwood & Jury

NEW COUNCIL OFFICES, BRITON FERRY, GLAM.
MOUNTCHARLES STONE DRESSINGS AND SHAMROCK STONE SHODDIES
Architect : H Alex. Clarke, Esq.

LOCH ESKE CASTLE, CO. DONEGAL, THE BEAUTIFUL RESIDENCE OF CAPTAIN WHITE.

THE DRESSINGS OF THE EXISTING BUILDING ARE WHOLLY OF MOUNTCHARLES STONE, WHICH IS ALSO BEING USED FOR THE EXTENSIONS NOW IN COURSE OF ERECTION.

Belfast Works.

In consequence of the increased demand for cut stone in Ireland and the difficulties of obtaining skilled labour in the remote districts where the Quarries are situate in Co. Donegal, it was last year resolved to establish a Works in the city of Belfast.

An ideal site has been secured for a long term of years from the Belfast Harbour Commissioners. It adjoins the Musgrave Channel abutting Harland Road, near the famous Shipbuilding Works of Messrs. Harland & Woolf, and has wharfage accommodation where Steamers can load and discharge at any state of the tide. The Works also have a direct Railway connection right into the centre of the yard. The situation and facilities are, therefore unique.

The Works have been laid out with the most modern Stone saw frames, planing and moulding machines, rubbing tables and other equipments for the sawing and preparation of all descriptions of Stonework. The machinery is driven by a powerful gas engine. Sheds for the accommodation of a large number of masons have been erected, together with offices, workshops and stores.

Masonry orders to any extent can be executed with promptitude from these works and distributed to all parts of Ireland. Block Stone from the Mountcharles Quarries, and also various descriptions of our English Stones are kept in stock in large quantities for immediate use, which ensures the prompt execution and despatch of all work.

VIEW OF MASONS' SHEDS, BELFAST WORKS.

MACHINERY AT MUSGRAVE CHANNEL WORKS, BELFAST

S.S. "HOPETOUN" LOADING A CARGO OF DRESSED STONE AT
MUSGRAVE CHANNEL WORKS, BELFAST.

Shamrock Stone.

These Quarries and Works have been taken over with the business of Messrs. G. A. Watson & Co., Limited ; together with the Luogh Quarries previously owned by the South Luogh Quarry Co., Ltd., and the Caherbarnagh Quarries previously worked by the Liscannor Quarry Co., Ltd., all producing similar quality materials.

The Stone is obtained from the Doonagore, Luogh and Caherbarnegh Quarries, situated near Liscannor in County Clare, on the West Coast of Ireland.

It is a hard, clean, close grained Blue Grey Mill-stone Grit, absolutely uniform in substance and colour, entirely free from nodules or hard bits of grit, such as are found in so many otherwise good Stones.

The self faced Flags are world famed, and cannot be surpassed for quality and wear. They are unquestionably the very best natural Stone Flags produced anywhere.

All sizes of Kerb and Channel are obtained, and for this purpose it is harder and superior to Granite.

The Block beds are sawn into Steps and Landings, and general Building purposes. For Staircases it is everlasting wear, and for any purpose where strength or wear is the principal feature, it is the very best Stone obtainable.

Excellent Setts and Building Shoddies are also supplied and worked in large quantities, and owing to the level beds and joints are very cheaply fixed.

Shamrock Stone does not wear slippery, and is admirably adapted for heavy traffic.

It is shipped from the Harbour at Liscannor (in proximity to the Quarries) into our own steamers, which are constantly running between Ireland and England, and thence distributed *ex* Steamer to any Town or Railway Station in the Country, or in smaller quantities from the Depots in London, South Wales and other places.

The Stone has been supplied largely to the Great Western Railway and other of the principal Railways in England for Paving, Steps and Platform Copings, also to the Offices of Works for Staircases, etc., at the Royal Mint, National Art Gallery and numerous Post Offices, and to many eminent Architects for Public Buildings. The Flags, and Kerb, and Channel are well known to all Surveyors.

The difficulty hitherto has been to secure satisfactory deliveries, but having re-organised the Quarries, and arranged for a very largely increased output, and having the control of our own Steamers, and established Depots in different Sea Ports for the distribution

No. 3 QUARRY FACE, DOONAGORE, CO. CLARE.

No. 3 QUARRY, DOONAGORE, CO. CLARE.

SHAMROCK STONE—Continued.

of the Stone, there is no longer any difficulty in getting any quantity or sizes with promptitude. This has already been appreciated and owing to its superiority over all other Street materials the demand is constantly and rapidly increasing.

ANALYSIS.

Silica	84.90
Alumina	6.60
Oxide of Iron	3.60
Oxide of Manganese	0.65
Lime	0.90
Magnesia	1.26
Sulphuric Acid	Trace
Carbonic Acid	Nil
Alkalies etc.	0.39
Water	1.70
	100.00

Crushing Strain (Kirkaldy) 2214 tons to the square foot.

SOUTH LUOGH QUARRY, CO. CLARE.

No. 2 QUARRY, DOONAGORE, CO. CLARE

No. 6 QUARRY, DOONAGORE, CO. CLARE.

GENERAL VIEW OF No. 2 QUARRY FACE, DOONAGORE

POST OFFICE AND PROPERTY AT DOONAGORE, CO CLARE.

WORKMEN'S
COTTAGES,
DOONAGORE,
CO. CLARE.

OFFICES
AND
STABLES,
DOONAGORE,
CO. CLARE.

WORKSHOPS,
DOONAGORE,
CO. CLARE.

TUNNELLING FOR FLAGSTONES, CAHERBARNAGH QUARRIES, CO. CLARE.

CAHERBARNAGH QUARRY, CO. CLARE.

STORAGE GROUND AND STOCKS OF SHAMROCK STONE,
LISCANNOR, CO. CLARE

SHAMROCK STONE AWAITING SHIPMENT,
LISCANNOR HARBOUR, CO CLARE.

Briton Ferry Depot.

This is a Yard established at the Great Western Railway Company's Dock at Briton Ferry in the County of Glamorganshire, on the borders of Swansea Bay.   It is principally used for distributing Shamrock Irish Stone, of which large stocks of Paving Flags, Kerb, Channel, Shoddies, Steps, Cills and Copings are always kept on hand for the prompt supply of general orders throughout South Wales, in which district there is a large daily demand. A stock of Porthgain Granite Chippings is also kept on hand.   It immediately adjoins the Dock-head, and vessels discharge direct on to the yard.   It is surrounded by Railway Sidings, with which it is directly connected.

These facilities make it an unique and useful central Depot for the execution of small orders in truck loads, thus avoiding heavy railway carriage, and providing cheap cost of transit for small lots.

STOCKS OF SHAMROCK STONE AT BRITON FERRY DEPOT, SOUTH WALES.

SHREWSBURY ROAD, BIRKENHEAD.
Paved with Shamrock Flags.

MAIN ENTRANCE TO ST. JOHN'S GARDENS, LIVERPOOL.
Shamrock Stone Steps and Landings.

WHITEHALL, S.W.
Shamrock Paving.

HIGH STREET, SWANSEA.
Shamrock Paving.
Borough Surveyor: C. Bell, Esq.

LAYING SHAMROCK PAVING KERB AND CHANNEL IN STREETS
AT PENYLAN, ROATH, CARDIFF.
City Surveyor: W Harpur, Esq.

DEVONSHIRE ROAD, BIRKENHEAD.
Shamrock Paving.

A STREET IN CARDIFF.
Laid with Shamrock Paving Kerb and Channel.

DE LANK CORNISH GRANITE.

De Lank Cornish Granite.

This celebrated Grey Cornish Granite comes from the enormous Quarries adjoining the De Lank River, near St. Breward, a few miles form Bodmin.   They have been purchased with all the equipment from the Hard Stone Firms, Ltd., of Bath.

The Quarries include the Rough Tor Mountain and 8,000 acres of land.   They are so extensive that the Granite obtainable is sufficient to do the whole of the Granite Trade of the Country for centuries, and the vast thickness and area of the beds make it an easy matter to obtain stones of any size, the handling being the only restriction in regard to dimensions. The large stones that can be cut is a special feature of the Quarries, and Blocks can be handled up to 20 tons weight.   De Lank Granite is pre-eminently sound, strong and imperishable, and of effective appearance.   The Quarries are splendidly equipped with Machinery and modern appliances for working and dealing with the Granite.

The water from the De Lank River is utilised as the motive power, and the Turbine is renowned as the largest and finest in the United Kingdom.   This Turbine drives an enormous Compressor Engine, also the extensive Saws, Polishers and Lathes in the Polishing Mills, which are amongst the best outside Aberdeen.   There are Lathes which can deal with Columns up to 27 feet long in one piece, and the Polishers can treat Granite of any dimensions and shape.   The whole of the numerous Cranes, Rock Drills and other appliances are worked by compressed air, and the extensive Masonry Sheds contain the most modern Surfacers and Pneumatic Tools for the use of the workmen.

The Quarries, Masonry Shops and Polishing Mills are all connected with the London and South Western Railway by a Railway Siding which runs from the face of the Quarries through the Masons' Yards and Works to an incline, which is worked by means of a large drum and endless rope, letting down the loaded wagons and pulling up the empties, from Wenford, where it joins the Wenford Mineral Branch of the London and South Western Railway system.

For Building purposes no more suitable Granite can be found.   Its light grey colour and pleasing appearance, and the fact that it admits of a high degree of polish, has made it the most popular Granite on the market for Fronts of Buildings, Steps, Landings and internal purposes.   Examples of its use for this class of work may be seen in London at the New General Post Office, Newgate Street, E.C. ; British Medical Institute, Strand, W.C. ;   Royal London Mutual Insurance Offices, Finsbury Square, ;   Electra House, Finsbury ;   Offices of the " Birmingham Daily Post," Fleet Street ;   Entrance Doorway and Steps at New Scotland Yard ;   Anglo-American Oil Company's New Offices, Queen Anne's Gate, etc. ;   also Messrs. Fry & Sons' new premises in Union Street, Bristol, and many other places in the Provinces.

DE LANK GRANITE QUARRIES, Nos. 1 and 2.

DE LANK GRANITE QUARRIES, Nos. 3, 4 and 5.

DE LANK CORNISH GRANITE—continued.

As an Engineering Granite it cannot be surpassed. The mean crushing strength is 1171 tons to the square foot, and its wonderful durability is evidenced by the fact that it is used by the Trinity House for its most exposed Lighthouses erected at Sea, such as the Eddystone, and the new Lighthouse at Beachy Head, and the Small Rocks Light, all of which were dressed and dry fixed at these Quarries. The Tower Bridge, London, is erected of De Lank Granite. A large quantity has also been used in the Thames Embankment. Many Docks have been constructed with Granite from these Quarries, including the new Alexandra Dock at Newport, Mon., just approaching completion.

For Monumental purposes it is in great demand, and the rapidly increasing sales in this department of the Works, is proof of its popularity amongst Sculptors for Tombs, Crosses, Headstones and Kerbs. A book of designs is published and will be forwarded free to anyone interested in the Monumental Branch of the business.

It is pleasing to relate that there is an increasing demand for British Granite for Street work including Kerbs, Channels, and Setts. De Lank is securing a fair share of this trade as owing to water and rail connections and the special facilities at the Quarries, it can be supplied at prices to compare favourably with foreign materials, whilst it is much harder and far superior in wearing qualities and does not get slippery.

Forced up between the Granite formation at these Quarries there are wide veins of Elvan, which are worked separately for Macadam purposes. Baxter's Breakers are in use and driven from the Turbine. The material is broken to gauges, stored in bins and loaded direct from these bins into railway trucks. The London and South Western Railway are large customers for this material, and the County and other Councils of Cornwall and adjoining Counties are ready purchasers of the surplus supplies, on account of its toughness and excellent wearing qualities.

The Ports of Shipment are Padstow and Wadebridge on the London and South Western Railway, and Fowey on the Great Western Railway.

F. Kitto & Son.
FOWEY, SHIPPING PORT FOR DE LANK GRANITE

VIEW
OF
FACE
No. 1 QUARRY,
DE LANK.

THE WORKING FACE OF No. 2 QUARRY AT DE LANK.

A LARGE POLISHED COLUMN, BASE AND CAP READY FOR DESPATCH,
DE LANK POLISHING MILLS.

POLISHING MILLS AND STONE-BREAKING MACHINERY, DE LANK.

TURNING A LATHE COLUMN FOR THE G.P.O. BUILDINGS, LONDON.
DE LANK WORKS.

MASONRY YARDS AND SHEDS, DE LANK.
Fitted Throughout with Pneumatic Surfacing machines and Tools.

TECHNICAL INSTITUTE, NEWPORT, MONMOUTHSHIRE.
PRINCIPAL ENTRANCE AND BASEMENT OF DE LANK GRANITE

Borough Architects: Charles F. Ward, Esq

VICTORIA STATION, MANCHESTER, L. & Y.R.
DE LANK GRANITE

BRITISH MEDICAL INSTITUTE, STRAND, W.C.

Ground, First and Second Floors of Cornish Granite from the De Lank Quarries

Architect : H. Percy Adams, Esq

MESSRS J. S. FRY & SONS' PREMISES, BRISTOL.
GROUND AND FIRST FLOORS BUILT OF CORNISH GRANITE FROM THE DE LANK QUARRIES.
Architects: Messrs. R. Milverton Drake & Pizey

OFFICES FOR THE ANGLO-AMERICAN OIL COMPANY,
QUEEN ANNES GATE, WESTMINSTER, S.W.

DE LANK GRANITE BASEMENT

Architects: Messrs. Ernest Runtz & Son.

GENERAL POST OFFICE EXTENSIONS,
ST. MARTINS-LE-GRAND, E.C.

DE LANK CORNISH GRANITE BASEMENT AND COLUMNS.

Architect: Sir Henry Tanner   Office of Works.

J. E. Oatey.

WADEBRIDGE: SHIPPING PORT FOR DE LANK GRANITE.

THE FAMOUS EDDYSTONE LIGHTHOUSE
ENTIRELY CONSTRUCTED OF GRANITE FROM THE
DE LANK QUARRIES

A TRAIN LOAD OF DE LANK GRANITE LEAVING WENFORD SIDINGS, L. & S.W.R

Dartmoor Granite.

The Company has acquired this extensive business carried on for many years by Duke & Co., Ltd., whose Head Offices were at Plymouth. The Quarries are situated at Merrivale, near Princetown, on Dartmoor in the County of Devon. The Property purchased contains a practically inexhaustible supply of the finest quality of Granite of regular colour and even texture sufficient to meet any demand which can be made. Blocks of any dimensions can be obtained and the Quarries and Works are well equipped with powerful Steam Cranes and modern Machinery for cutting and working orders of all kinds. The Polishing Plant and Smiths' Forges are driven by a Turbine, the water being stored in a large reservoir on the top of the hill.

The Granite is suitable for all purposes and is extensively supplied for Dock, Harbour and Engineering work, Architectural and Monumental requirements, and for Building and Street purposes.

Dartmoor Granite from these Quarries has been used in the construction of great Public Works, such as the Thames Embankment, most of the London Bridges, the recent widening of London Bridge, and Blackfriars Bridge, Admiralty Dockyard Extensions and other large Dock and Harbour Works.

The Granite used in the new Entrance to the Coal Dock at Hartlepool for the North Eastern Railway Company has been recently supplied from these Quarries. The dimensions of the blocks were exceptionally large and the material and workmanship has given the greatest satisfaction to all concerned.

It is a material in great demand for large public Memorials. The Granite in the Nelson Monument was supplied from these Quarries, also the National Memorial to the Martyrs at Canterbury, the National War Memorial at Aldershot, and the exceptionally fine War Memorial at Bolton erected a short time ago.

It is an excellent material for Building purposes, and can be supplied for fronts of Buildings, also Steps and Landings at favourable prices.

Kerb, Channel and Setts for Road work represents a good proportion of the output, and with special facilities at commend it is hoped to compete successfully with Foreign Granite in most parts of England and Wales.

Experts and famous authorities say no better Granite can be obtained, it having been supplied with complete satisfaction to all parts of the country.

With our exceptional advantages and great resources we hope and expect to be able to secure orders for all kind of work in all the markets.

Included in the purchase of this business is the Depot at Victoria Wharves, Sutton Road, Plymouth, where large stocks of Granite, as well as other Stones will always be kept for local requirements. This Depot also serves as a distributing centre for the West of England, and will be used in connection with the shipment of cargoes of Granite from the Dartmoor Quarries, Plymouth being the nearest post of shipment.

MERRIVALE GRANITE QUARRIES, DARTMOOR.

MERRIVALE GRANITE QUARRIES, DARTMOOR.

STOCKS OF GRANITE SETTS, VICTORIA WHARVES, PLYMOUTH.

GRANITE CORBELLS FOR LONDON BRIDGE.
Dartmoor Quarries

BLACKFRIARS BRIDGE WIDENING.
Dartmoor Granite from the Merrivale Quarries

ENTRANCE TO NEW COAL DOCK, WEST HARTLEPOOL, FOR THE NORTH EASTERN RAILWAY Co
Dartmoor Granite from Our Merrivale Quarries.

SOUTH AFRICAN
WAR MEMORIAL
NOW ERECTED AT
BOLTON, LANCASHIRE.

Showing the Monument
Dry-built in the Quarry
ready for despatch.

DARTMOOR GRANITE

WITH POLISHED SURFACES

AN ABUTMENT OF BLACKFRIARS BRIDGE.
DARTMOOR GRANITE.

OFFICES OF THE AMALGAMATED SOCIETY OF
RAILWAY SERVANTS, EUSTON ROAD, N.W..
DARTMOOR GRANITE.

BLUE BRISTOL PENNANT STONE.

Bristol Pennant Stone.

It is a hard Sandstone of a pleasing Blue colour. The Quarries are extensive, and are situated at Fishponds, Stapleton, Hallatrow, and Winterbourne, near Bristol. Those at the first named places have been largely worked for many years by the Hard Stone Firms, Ltd., (whose head offices were at Bath). At Fishponds there is a large Works well equipped with modern machinery for Sawing and Working the Stone, with Masonry Sheds, and at Hallatrow there is a private Railway Siding running right into the Quarry. The Huckford Quarry at Winterbourne adjoining the main line of the Great Western Railway was re-opened a couple of years ago by the Forest of Dean Stone Firms, Ltd.

The value of Pennant Stone is well known to all Surveyors for Street Kerb, Channel, Crossings and Setts, and to Architects and Engineers for all classes of work.

Kerb and Channel is a speciality of these Quarries and is sent away in large quantities to all parts of the country. It is now in great demand in preference to foreign Granite, being cheaper and quite as good and durable. It is prepared with the exposed surfaces, either Straight Pointed, or Random Pointed or Bunched (Tooled), the latter workmanship being a little more expensive than the former. The Quarries yield stone of splendid lengths which enables us to supply a good average size and it can be readily split to any dimensions.

Shoddies, Walling Stone, and Pitching are largely supplied and the Quarries are equipped with stone breakers for dealing with Broken Stone for concrete and ballasting purposes.

A good trade is carried on for Girder Bedstones, String Courses, Copings, Caps and Engineering work generally, for which purpose it cannot be surpassed owing to its exceptional strength and durability.

For Steps, and Landings, Basements to Buildings, Dressings and Building work of all kinds it is in great favour and has been extensively used by the Government and Public Bodies in many of their most important Buildings in different parts of the Kingdom. It is a perfect weather resisting stone, does not wear slippery, and can be quarried in Blocks of any dimensions. Sawn Paving is a speciality. Although a very hard stone with the aid of Machinery it can now be supplied for any class of work at a very low cost.

It is in good demand for Monumental purposes owing to its uniformity of colour and very fine grain.

A Pink colour Stone (called locally Red Pennant) is obtained from some of the beds in some of the Quarries, and is preferred to the Blue by some Architects and Surveyors. This too can be supplied for any purpose and in any sizes and quantities. It is slightly harder than the Blue and equally durable.

MANOR ROAD QUARRIES, FISHPONDS, BRISTOL.

No 2 QUARRY, FISHPONDS, BRISTOL

BROOM HILL QUARRIES, STAPLETON, BRISTOL

FISHPONDS WORKS, BRISTOL.
A VIEW OF THE MACHINERY.

SIDING QUARRY, HALLATROW.
BLUE PENNANT STONE

QUARRYING BLUE PENNANT STONE AT HALLATROW

TEMPLE CLOUD QUARRIES, HALLATROW

A STREET IN CHIPPENHAM, WILTS.
SHOWING BLUE BRISTOL PENNANT STONE.

ANOTHER STREET IN CHIPPENHAM
BLUE PENNANT KERB.

FIREPLACE,
LINGHOLM
MANSION.
KESWICK

BLUE
BRISTOL
PENNANT
STONE

EXTENSION TO LINGHOLM MANSION, KESWICK, WESTMORELAND, THE RESIDENCE OF
SIR GEORGE KEMP, M.P.
BLUE BRISTOL PENNANT STONE

111

NEW SCHOOLS
FISHPONDS,
BRISTOL.

BLUE
PENNANT
STONE
FROM
OUR
FISHPONDS
QUARRIES.

CO-OPERATIVE WHOLESALE SOCIETY'S PREMISES, BRISTOL.
ENTIRE BASEMENT OF BLUE PENNANT STONE FROM THE FISHPONDS QUARRIES

112

CO-OPERATIVE WHOLESALE SOCIETY'S PREMISES, BRISTOL.
MAIN ENTRANCE DOORWAY, ON THE QUAY

BLUE BRISTOL PENNANT STONE.

BAILEY QUARRY, CHARLTON MACKEREL.

A ROADWAY, RUSH CORNER ESTATE, BOURNEMOUTH.
WITH A VIEW OF KEINTON STONE KERB AND CHANNEL.

Keinton and Street Stones.

These are hard Blue Lias Limestones obtained from a number of scattered Quarries in the vicinity of Keinton Mandeville, Charlton and Street (near Glastonbury), Somersetshire. A lot of this property is Freehold, which reduces the cost of production. It was previously owned by the Hard Stone Firms, Ltd., of Bath.

The quarries have been worked for over a thousand years, they produce excellent stone which lies near the surface in layers varying in thickness from ½ to 10 inches thick and can be obtained in almost any sizes.

Owing chiefly to natural advantages it can be quarried cheaper than any other kind of stone, and the selling prices are therefore extremely low. It also lends itself to easy conversion rendering the dressing cost very reasonable and the finished workmanship is of a very neat appearance. It has always borne a good reputation on the market as (although cheap) it is a reliable and durable material. This explains its popularity and after being used for hundreds of years the demand for the stone to-day is greater than ever.

To Surveyors who are not able to afford the cost of Granite or Hard Sandstones such as Shamrock or Pennant, it is especially suitable and it will be found eminently satisfactory in cost, quality, durability and workmanship.

Its principal uses are for Paving and other Flags, Kerbing, Channelling, Villa Steps, Landings, Cills, Copings, Shoddies, etc.

Excellent testimonials can be furnished from Surveyors, who have used this Stone for a great number of years with the greatest satisfaction and many of whom assert that they have never met with any material which they think better for general Street work. It has been regularly supplied for years to most of the Towns and Villages in the West and South of England, and excellent examples can be seen almost everywhere in these parts of the country.

HYDE QUARRY, KEINTON MANDEVILLE

STEPSTONES QUARRY, KEINTON MANDEVILLE.

CHESSELS QUARRY, KEINTON.

STACKING GROUND AND MASONS' SHEDS, HARPITTS QUARRY, KEINTON.

HARPITTS QUARRY, KEINTON MANDEVILLE.

KNIGHT'S QUARRY, KEINTON MANDEVILLE

OVERLEIGH QUARRY, STREET.

No. 1 QUARRY, STREET

WINTER RECREATION GROUND, BOURNEMOUTH.
Keinton Kerb and Channel

A STREET IN PLYMOUTH.
Paved with Keinton Stone.

RESIDENCE OF F. P. PITMAN, ESQ.,
KEINTON MANDEVILLE.
BUILT ENTIRELY OF KEINTON STONE

A BRIDGE ON THE CASTLE CARY TO LANGPORT
G. W. RAILWAY
ASHLAR FROM THE STREET QUARRIES

NEW SCHOOLS, ABERDARE.
KEINTON STONE SHODDIES
Architect : J. H. Phillips, Esq

Porthgain Granite

For MACADAM and CHIPPINGS.

Mr J. S. Flett of the Museum of Practical Geology, London, has tested and made a report upon specimens of this material. He quotes from Mr. J. V. Elsden who has made a special study of the igneous rocks of this part of Pembrokeshire. Mr. Elsden gives the following description of the Porthgain Rock (Quarterly Journal of the Geological Society, Volume LXI, p 592, 1905). The minerals present are apatite, ilmenite, augite, felspar, rhombic pyroxene and quartz. Apatite is abundant. The augite clearly precedes both the felspar and rhombic pyroxine. It is granular and is included in, or moulds, both the last-named minerals. Rhombic pyroxene, however, crystallised later than the felspar, by which it is penetrated. It occurs in rather ragged rectangular sections and is faintly pleochronic. A large portion of the felspar has rather a low refractive index and a sym-metrical extinction of nearly 20 degrees in twins on the albite plan ; it is therefore, probably albite. A little orthoclase of later crystallization appears to be present. Quartz is fairly abundant in small interstitial grains, clusters of which extinguish simultaneously, but there is no micropegmatite. From its greater acidity the rock may therefore be classed as a quartz-enstatite diorite. It is of a somewhat unusual type and difficult to classify.

A representation is shewn of the photomicrograph of this rock by Mr. J. V. Elsden, and which is reproduced by the courtesy of Mr. J. Allen Howe, Curator of the Geological Survey of England and Wales, Jermyn Street, S.W.

It is of a peculiarly tough nature which, with its extreme hardness, makes wonderful roads, and it has already won the reputation of being equal to any road material on the market. Besides its exceptional durability, under wear it furnishes a non-slippery road and leaves the surface almost entirely free from dust and mud at all times. Another important feature is the specific gravity, which is 2.80, and gives a greater covering capacity than most of the other best-class road materials.

The Quarries are situated on the Coast of Pembrokeshire about midway between St. David's Head and Strumble Head, in the Parish of Llanrhian. During the past few years they have been extensively developed and the quality of the prime beds now opened up and being worked has exceeded the most sanguine expectations. A Railway has been constructed to convey the Granite by locomotive from the Quarries to the Breakers, and the Quarries are equipped with a new and powerful compressed air plant for working the Drills and Machinery. An extensive Breaking Plant has also been laid down comprising Baxters, Broadbents, and Hadfield's Breakers of the latest and most improved types, together with modern appliances for handling and loading the Granite with a minimum of hand labour.

A FACE OF GRANITE AT PORTHGAIN QUARRIES.

ANOTHER VIEW OF PORTHGAIN GRANITE QUARRIES.

PORTHGAIN GRANITE—Continued.

A supplementary Plant has recently been erected to deal with the small gauges. By means of a Zimmer Conveyor all the surplus smalls are conveyed, elevated and put through a double set of Rolls, and special Screens of the most modern pattern, supplied and erected by Messrs. Ord &Maddison. This produces specially screened small gauges, perfectly clean and free from dust, which are stored separately in large quantities ready for shipment. The quality of these Screenings cannot be surpassed for Granolithic, Ferro Concrete, Artificial Paving and Stonework, and other uses.

Adjoining the Quarries is the Porthgain Harbour, which is part of the Freehold Property. Large Storage Bins have been constructed, and from which the Granite is loaded direct into vessels alongside. The harbour is capable of accommodating four vessels on each tide, and steamers up to 400 tons carrying capacity are loaded daily. We possess our own fleet of steamers which assures prompt and regular supplies.

The Granite Macadam is broken and screened to gauges of 2½ inches, 2 inches, 1½ inches, and 1 inch.

For binding purposes mixed Chippings of ¾ inches down to ¼ inch are stored, and also ¼ inch down to dust. The specially Screened Chippings for Granolithic and Ferro Concrete work are stocked in sizes of ⅝, ½, ⅜, and ⅛ down to dust.

An Attrition Test of the material has been made by E. J. Lovegrove, Esq., the well-known Borough Surveyor of Hornsey, who reports as follows :—

Reference No.	Description of Stone.	Hand (H) or Machine (M) Broken.	Chips. Percentage detached from Parent Stone.		Dust. Percentage of Loss.		Average.	Specific Gravity.
			Dry Test.	Wet Test.	Dry Test.	Wet Test.		
193	Porthgain Granite from Porthgain, North of Llanrhian, Pembrokeshire	M.	.0	.0	.20	9.47	7.84	2.80

Amongst the principal users are :—

The County Councils of Somersetshire, Gloucestershire, Glamorganshire, Monmouthshire, Wiltshire, Pembrokeshire, Cardiganshire, Kent, East Sussex, West Sussex, Surrey, and Cambridgeshire.

The Corporations of Southend-on-Sea, Woodwich, Bridgwater, Barnstaple, Bristol, Newport, Swansea, Cardiff, Llanelly, Haverfordwest, Neath, Pembroke, Rye, Battersea, Glastonbury and Faversham.

ANOTHER WORKING GALLERY AT PORTHGAIN.

LOWER GALLERIES, PORTHGAIN GRANITE QUARRIES.

PORTHGAIN GRANITE—Continued.

The Urban District Councils of Barry, Briton Ferry, Burnham, Bradford-on-Avon, Burry Port, Cardigan, Minehead, Neyland, Highbridge, Lynton, Weston-super-Mare, Bognor, Newcastle Emlyn, Newquay, Mutford, and Lothingland, Lowestoft, Broadstairs, and St. Peters, Dorking, Milford Haven, Pontypridd, Epsom, Penge, Watchet, Grays-Thurrock, Portland and Loughton.

The Rural District Councils of Bridgwater, Cuckfield, Neath, Keynsham, Rye, Steyning East, Sevenoaks, Thakeham, Uckfield, Wellington, Llantrissant, Llantwit Vardre, Horsham, Isle of Thanet, Williton, Guildford, East Ashford, Bath, Clutton, Axbridge, Wheatenhurst and Shepton Mallet.

PHOTOMICROGRAPH OF PORTGAIN GRANITE

Porthgain Bricks.

These Bricks are manufactured from Slate Shale, which is obtained from a large Quarry a few hundred yards from Porthgain Harbour. An extensive Brick Works with a large Hoffman Kiln have been erected on the Harbour, and the Works contain modern machinery, which produces an excellent Red Brick of natural colour. The Bricks are supplied in four qualities :—Best Pressed ; Seconds Pressed ; First Quality Wire Cuts and Second Quality Wire Cuts. On account of the excellent quality of the production, and the ready means of transit by water, there is a large demand for these bricks at all seaports in the Bristol Channel.

The Plant and Machinery have recently been greatly extended, and it is now hoped that a market may be found for them on the South Coast and in London, as well as in Dublin and the South of Ireland.

PORTHGAIN BRICK-WORKS

SPECIAL SCREENING PLANT AT PORTHGAIN
FOR GRADING CHIPPINGS.

WORKMEN'S INSTITUTE AND READING ROOMS,
PORTHGAIN.

PORTHGAIN—CRUSHING PLANT AND BINS.

AIR COMPRESSOR, PORTHGAIN QUARRIES.

S.S. "DEAN FOREST" LOADING MACADAM AT PORTHGAIN HARBOUR.

Shipping Department.

The consideration of the facilities of transport and delivery of the Firm's various productions by water has received very special attention. Porthgain Granite Macadam and Chippings are almost entirely water borne, and a large sea borne trade is conducted at the Shamrock Quarries, County Clare, and the Mountcharles Quarries, County Donegal, in conveying Stone from Ireland to England as also a considerable quantity of Portland Block Stone is conveyed by water from the Isle of Portland to Ports in all parts of the United Kingdom.

It was felt that chartered vessels would not be satisfactory to our customers to ensure regular and prompt deliveries, and in order to control supplies in an effectual manner the Directors decided to build and acquire a Fleet of Steamers.

As a result of this decision a contract was placed with Messrs. Smith's Dock Co., Ltd., of South Bank and Middlesbrough for five new Steel Screw Coasting Steamers, designed to fulfil the requirements of our trade, and these were constructed under the supervision of our Marine Surveyors, Captain Edward Hall & Sons, of Cardiff. The whole of these Steamers were completed and delivered to us at different periods of last year and are now in commission. They have been constructed with special consideration for the various ports to which they trade, and were specially strengthened for taking the ground. The registered names and deadweight of these vessels are :—

S/S " Porthgain "	350 tons, deadweight.
S/S " Mountcharles "	ditto.
S/S " Dean Forest "	ditto.
S/S " Liscannor "	ditto.
S/S " Multistone "	ditto.

The following are their dimensions :—

Length between perpendiculars...	130' 0"
Breadth	25' 0"
Depth Moulded	10' 0"

They are designed to carry a deadweight of about 350 tons on a draft of 10' 6", and are fitted with compound surface condensing engines having cylinders of 16'—34" x 24" stroke, and one boiler of 12' 0" diameter x 10' 0" long, with a working pressure of 130-lb. per square inch, of sufficient power to give vessels a speed of 8½ knots loaded.

The vessels are classed Lloyds 100 A.1. for coasting service, with long raised quarter-deck, short bridge and topgallant forecastle, and specially constructed for loading and discharging aground.

S.S. "MULTISTONE."

PORTHGAIN HARBOUR.

SHIPPING DEPARTMENT—Continued.

They have one large clear hold and hatchway, also powerful steam winches and derricks for handling large blocks rapidly, both in loading and discharging.

Specially large fore and aft peak tanks are fitted, with a total capacity of about 80 tons, for trimming purposes when vessels are running light.

Accommodation is fitted up under the bridge deck for the captain and mate, with neat saloon.

Engineers are berthed in Deck House at the after end of engine and boiler casing, with separate mess room adjacent to engine room.

Crew's quarters are in the topgallant forecastle.

In addition to these new Steamers we have purchased the :—
     S/S " Volana "   280 tons deadweight.
     S/S " Hopetown " 100   ditto.

This gives us a fleet of seven Steamers constantly dealing with the transport of our productions, and which enables us to execute all our seaborne orders with promptitude and regularity.

S.S. " DEAN FOREST " LOADING SHAMROCK STONE
LISCANNOR HARBOUR. CO. CLARE.

S.S. "MOUNTCHARLES."

STEAMERS LOADING MACADAM AT PORTHGAIN HARBOUR.

London Works and Depots.

These Wharves have been recently acquired from the old-established firm of Grice & Co., Ltd., together with all the Machinery, Plant, Effects, Goodwill and Stocks of Stone of every description.

These depots are connected by private Sidings with the Great Western Railway, London and North Western Railway, Midland Railway, and other Railway Lines.

There are Sand Saw Frames for cutting up any description of Stone, driven by Electric Motors, and an Electric Gantry commands the Addison Wharf.

These depots are specially used for the continuance of the large merchants trade which has been conducted by our predecessors for many years past, for Caen, York, and all kinds of Stone, also Marble, Granite and Alabaster, of which large stocks are always kept on hand for the immediate execution of all orders, which are supplied at lowest London prices.

A very valuable connection was built up by Messrs. Grice & Co., Ltd., amongst Sculptors and Monumental Masons, for the supply of specially selected and prime quality material for Monumental and Sculptural work, and every effort will be made to retain this connection, and to supply all customers to their satisfaction.

Adjoining these Wharves are our principal Stables in London, where a number of horses are kept for distributing materials in any quantities to all parts of the Metropolis with our own wagons.

A suite of Offices abut Warwick Road, where the principal Staff is kept to deal with the London section of the business.

KENSINGTON OFFICES AND ENTRANCE TO ADDISON WHARF,
WARWICK ROAD, W.

ADDISON WHARF AND WORKS, 191, WARWICK ROAD, KENSINGTON, W.

DEPOTS AT G.W.R., KENSINGTON, S.W.

A DIAMOND CIRCULAR SAW AT CROWN WORKS, S.W.

Crown Wharf,

69, LOTS ROAD, CHELSEA, S.W.

This Wharf adjoins Chelsea Creek, and vessels up to 150 tons carrying capacity can come alongside and be discharged with our own cranes.

A large quantity of modern machinery is erected at this Depot, which comprises Sand Saws, Diamond Circular Saws, Planing and Moulding Machines, Rubbing Tables, with powerful Cranes, driven by a suction gas plant, with the town gas connected as a reserve supply.

Substantial Masonry Shops have been erected to accommodate a large number of masons, together with Fitting Shops, Smiths' Shops, Workshops and necessary Offices for conducting a large Masonry Trade.

The situation of these Works and the modern machinery, with direct water access places us in an unique position to undertake masonry work in London. Any description of work in any class of stone can be executed with promptitude, prepared ready for setting, and if desired it can be fixed and cleaned down complete by our own workmen, for which purpose a large staff of competent fitters are constantly employed.

CROWN WHARF, 69, LOTS ROAD, CHELSEA, S.W.

CROWN WORKS, 69, LOTS ROAD, CHELSEA, S.W.

VIEW OF MASONS' SHOPS AT CROWN WORKS, CHELSEA, S.W.

Chelsea Wharf,

LOTS ROAD, S.W.

This extensive Wharf adjoins the before-mentioned Works, and until recently was in the occupation of Messrs. Eastwood & Co., Ltd., from whom we have taken it over upon a long lease. It has a long water frontage to Chelsea Creek ; double access to Lots Road, and closely adjoins Chelsea Basin, Great Western Railway Goods Station.

This Wharf is practically used for storage of Block Stone, also Porthgain Granite Chippings and Screenings, Shamrock (Irish) Paving Flags, and Street Kerb and Channel.

The Block Stone is discharged direct from vessel by a powerful Electric Derrick Crane, and large stocks of excellent quality Block Stone in good average sizes from the Portland, Forest of Dean, Red Wilderness, Nailsworth and other Quarries are always kept on hand. By this means London customers can go and select the sizes and quality suitable for their work, and with our own horses and wagons delivery can be made to any part of London at short notice.

Large storage bins have been constructed at this Wharf where Porthgain Granite Chippings in gauges of ⅝″, ½″, ⅜″, ¼″ and ¾″ to ¼″ mixed, also ⅛″ to dust, are always kept on hand for immediate delivery in large or small quantities. These Chippings are supplied at lowest London prices and the quality cannot be surpassed for Granolithic, Ferro Concrete and any artificial uses.

The remainder of this Wharf is taken up with stocks of excellent quality Irish Self-faced Paving Flags, and also Kerb and Channel from the celebrated Shamrock Quarries, which enables us to execute all orders for London and district by road deliveries with propmptitude, and from which centre the material can be distributed from the adjoining Goods Station to any of the suburbs or surrounding counties.

The Stone can be mason dressed at the Wharf if required and prepared to any specification, or to customers' requirements ready for setting.

STONE SAWS AND PLANING MACHINES AT CHELSEA WORKS, S.W.

CHELSEA DEPOT, CHELSEA CREEK, S.W.

Stewarts Road Works,

MIDLAND RAILWAY WHARF, WANDSWORTH ROAD, S.W.

These Masonry Works were formerly the property of Messrs. Webber & Corben, from whom they have been acquired. Like the other London Works this Yard is well equipped with Stone saw Frames, Planing and Moulding Machinery, Rubbing Tables, and other working plant for stone sawing and dressing. The whole of the Machinery is driven by a suction gas plant with the town gas supply as a reserve, and the Yard is commanded the whole length by a powerful Gantry electrically driven.

There are excellent Masons' Sheds with Workshops with Offices and other appliances for the preparation and prompt execution of all kinds of Masonry Work.

These Works have been acquired as an acquisition to the other Yards in London, in consequence of the increased demand for our different kinds of stones to be prepared in the London area ready for fixing.

Direct railway accommodation adjoins the Wharf and with access to Stewarts Road. Block Stone can be delivered to the Depot at a minimum cost, and when sawn or worked can be distributed by road or rail to any part of London.

It will be seen that these several Works and Depots with the large quantity of modern plant with which they are equipped places us in the front rank for the supply of worked stone in London, and enables us to deal with orders of any size and quantity in any specified time to suit the requirements of the work.

General Remarks.

All the different building stones are supplied in Random or Dimension Block, or Sand Sawn to sizes, or dressed ready for setting, and delivered to any Railway Station or Port in any part of the World.

We also undertake any description of Stonework fixed and cleaned down complete, for which purpose experienced fixers are constantly employed, and are available for any part of the Country at the shortest notice.

Kerb, Channel, Paving and other Stone for Surveyors' purposes is supplied either in the Rough, or Dressed to any required specification ready for laying, or we are prepared to contract for the materials laid complete if desired.

All Estimates are given free of cost, and information of every kind is readily furnished on application.

The whole of our Quarries in all parts of the Country have been well developed at very great cost, and all our Works are fully equipped with the most modern Plant, which enables us to quote exceptionally low prices, and to guarantee quick despatch of large or small orders.

Samples of either or all of our products are supplied gratis.

A number of practical and experienced Representatives are resident in every district, solely in our employ, who will be pleased to call and confer with you in regards to any business you may have in view. These Representatives cover the whole of England, Wales and Ireland, and are always at the services of our customers.

All Correspondence should be addressed to the Head Office in Bristol.

When you are in the market for Stone or Granite for Building, Engineering, or Monumental purposes, or for Street Work, or for Macadam or Chippings, we shall be very glad if you will kindly communicate with us, and we can give you first-class quality materials of any colour or variety, at very low prices, and guarantee best material and workmanship with very prompt delivery.

Our principal aim is to please our customers and give complete satisfaction in every way.

International Building Trades Exhibition,

Olympia, London,

. . . 1911 . . .

An Illustration is given herein of our Exhibit at this Exhibition.

IN submitting to the professions and trades the numerous examples of Building and other stones which emanate from our various Quarries we endeavoured to convey by the erection of a substantial structure, their suitability and adaptability for all classes of buildings, paving, etc.

The classical Pavilion designed to display our products achieved this object by its architectural features and merit, and indicated that a combination of variously tinted stones may be utilised with artistic advantage, under suitable conditions, in contradistinction to homogenity of each material and regularity in colour.

The variety of Stones used gave an added interest to the design, and Architects, Builders, and others were able to analyse the detail and better judge for themselves by seeing the stones *in situ* the general and individual effect far better than by merely inspecting and handling an ordinary sample block.

The name of each kind of stone was clearly marked on the structure, and information as to crushing strength, chemical analysis, and maximum dimensions of blocks was obtainable from our Representatives, in addition to a list of the numerous Buildings where our material has been used.

The Stones selected for the geometrical paving were those we recommend as being the hardest wearing and most suitable for the purpose, and in the scheme of colouring it was our endeavour to avoid violent contrasts, whilst the blending of tints was not so marked as in the more definitely figured, coloured, and more expensive material of marble.

International Building Trades Exhibition,

Olympia, London,

. . . 1911 . . .

Stand No. 146.

TYPOGRAPHIC AND IMAGE CONSERVATION, ARTWORK AND PRODUCTION BY DAVIES - WISE DESIGN COMPANY. WWW.DWDC.CO.UK